My

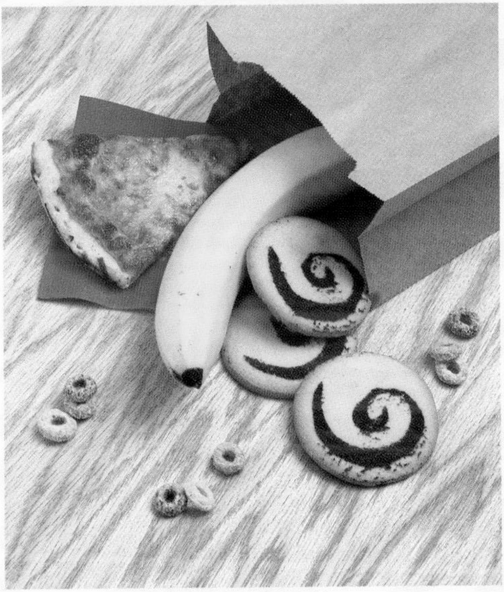

Patricia Almada

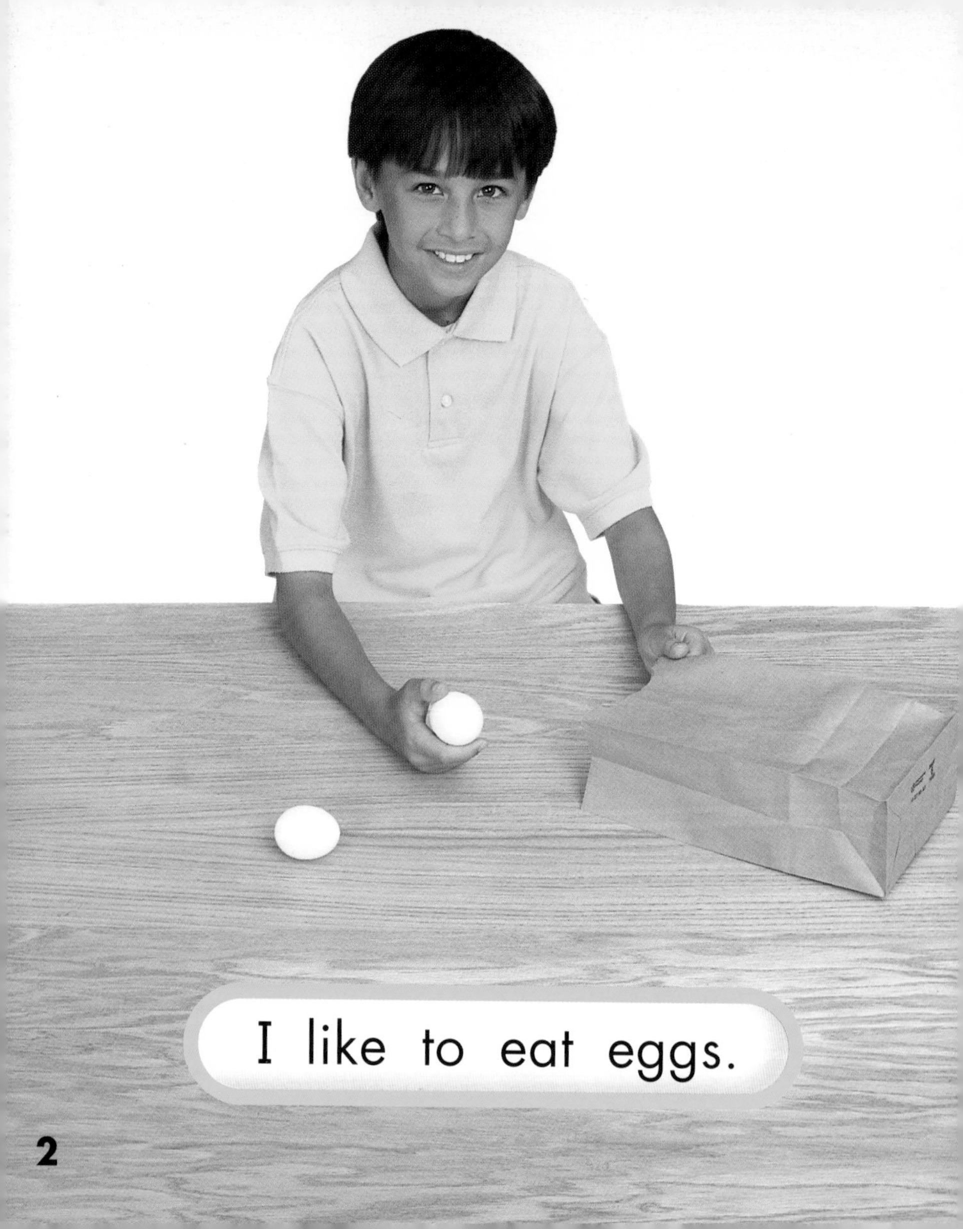

I like to eat eggs.

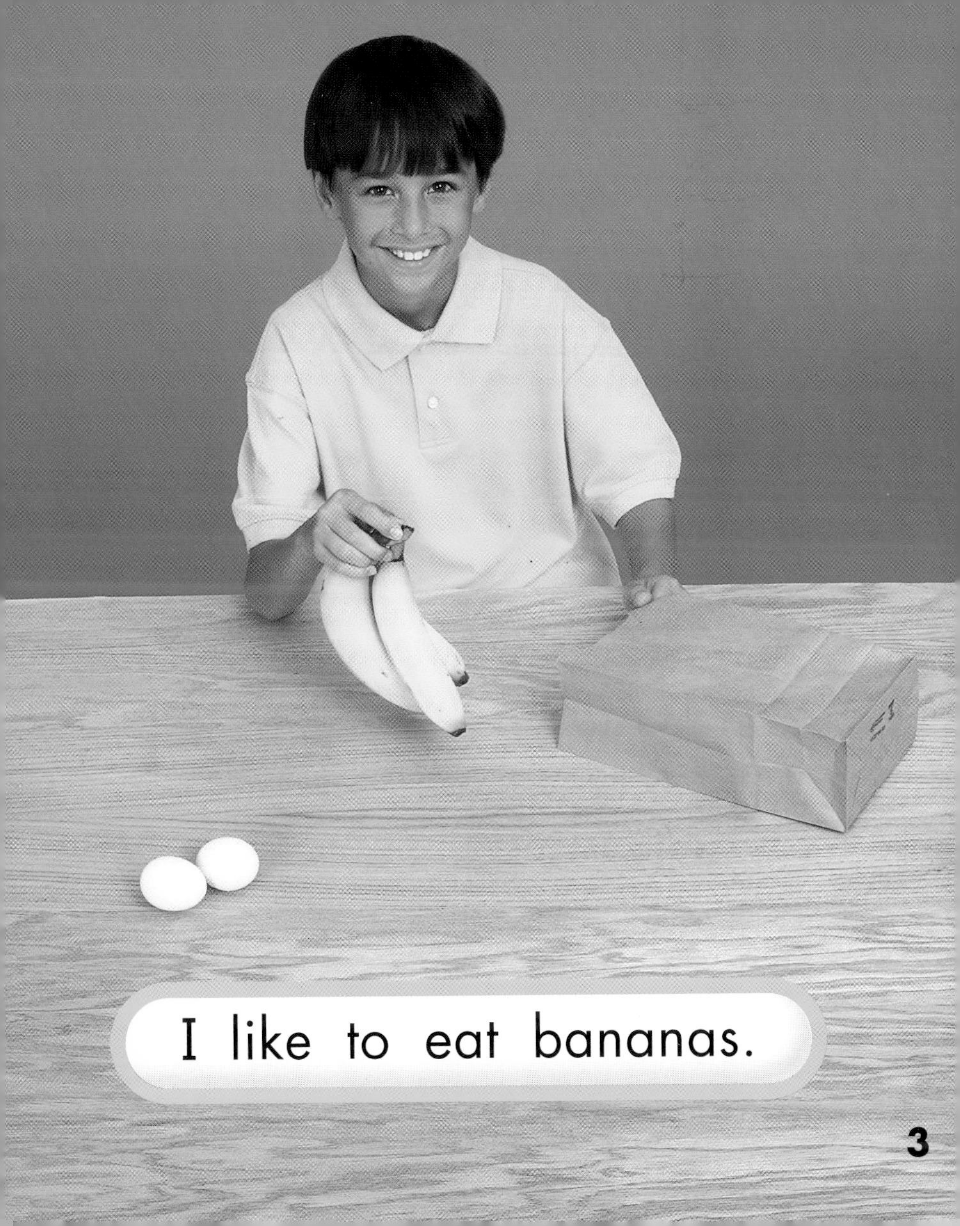

I like to eat bananas.

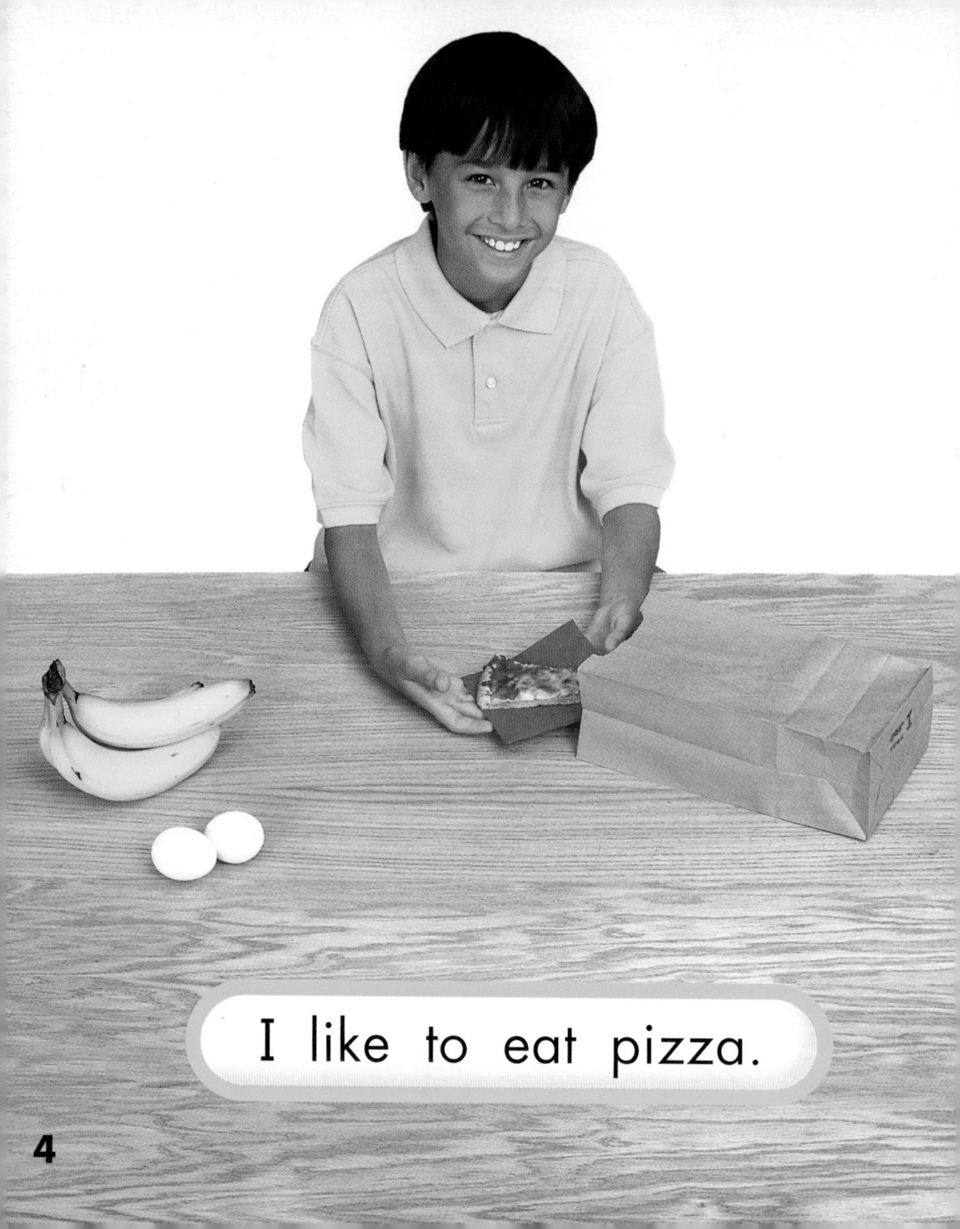

I like to eat pizza.

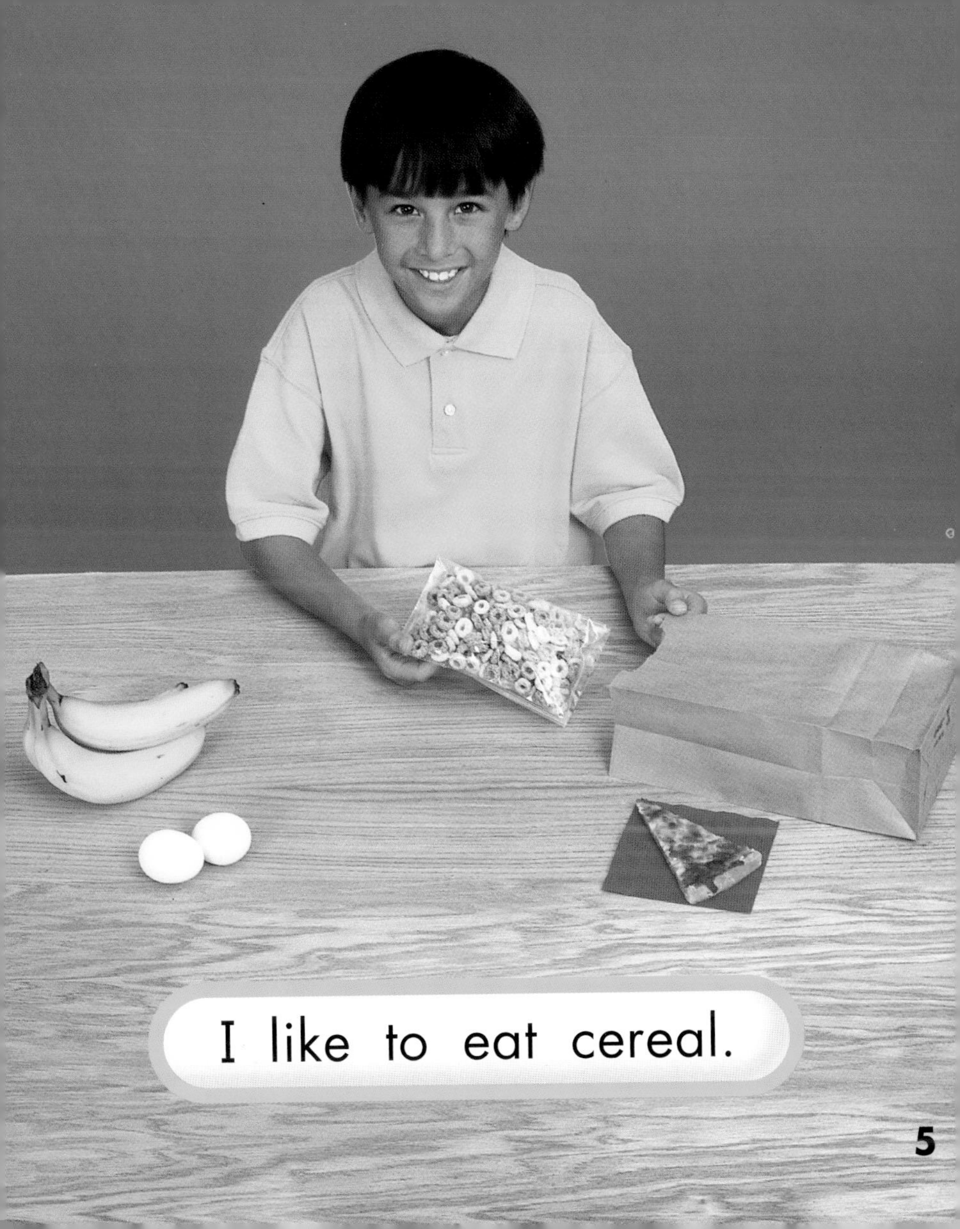

I like to eat cereal.

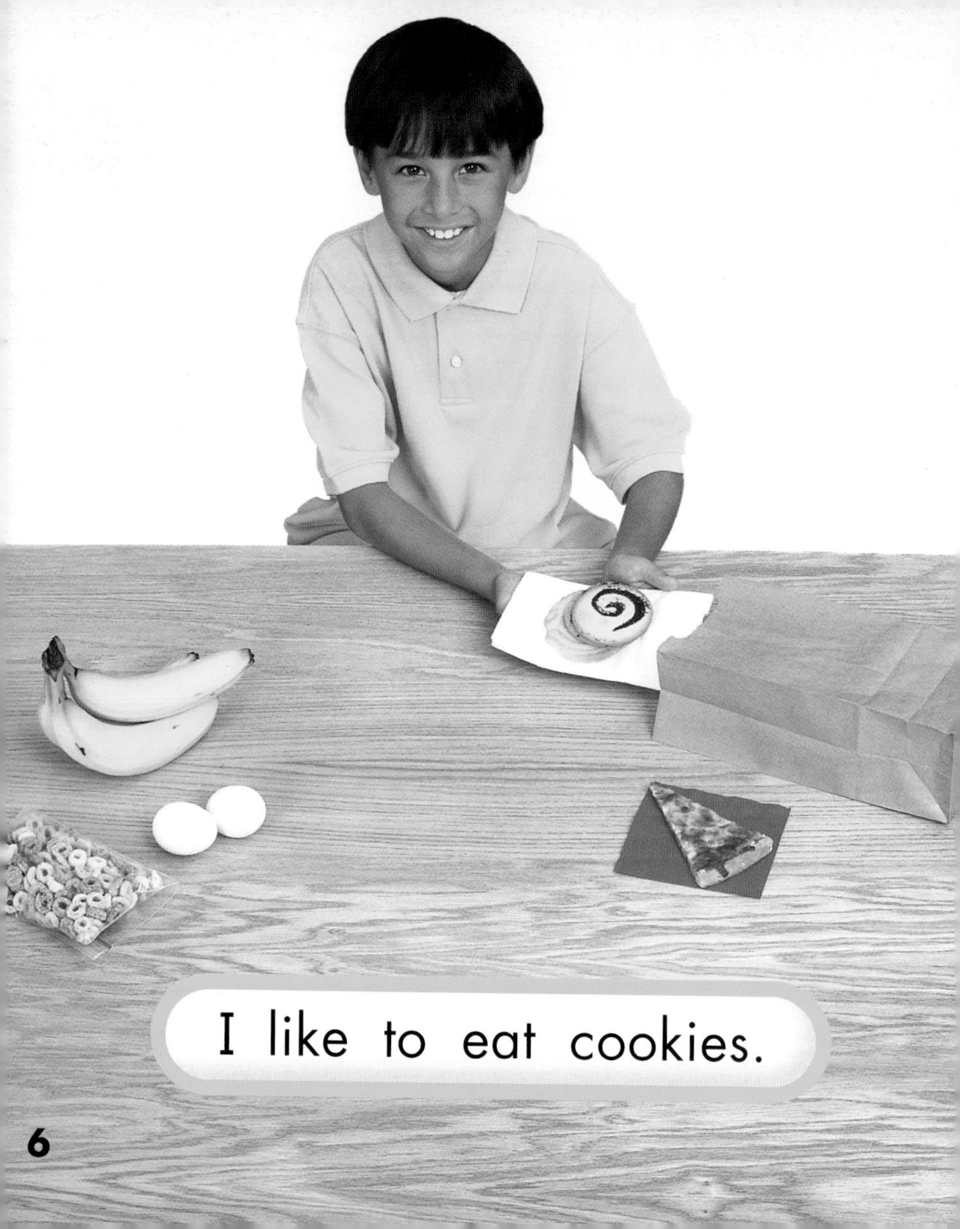

I like to eat cookies.

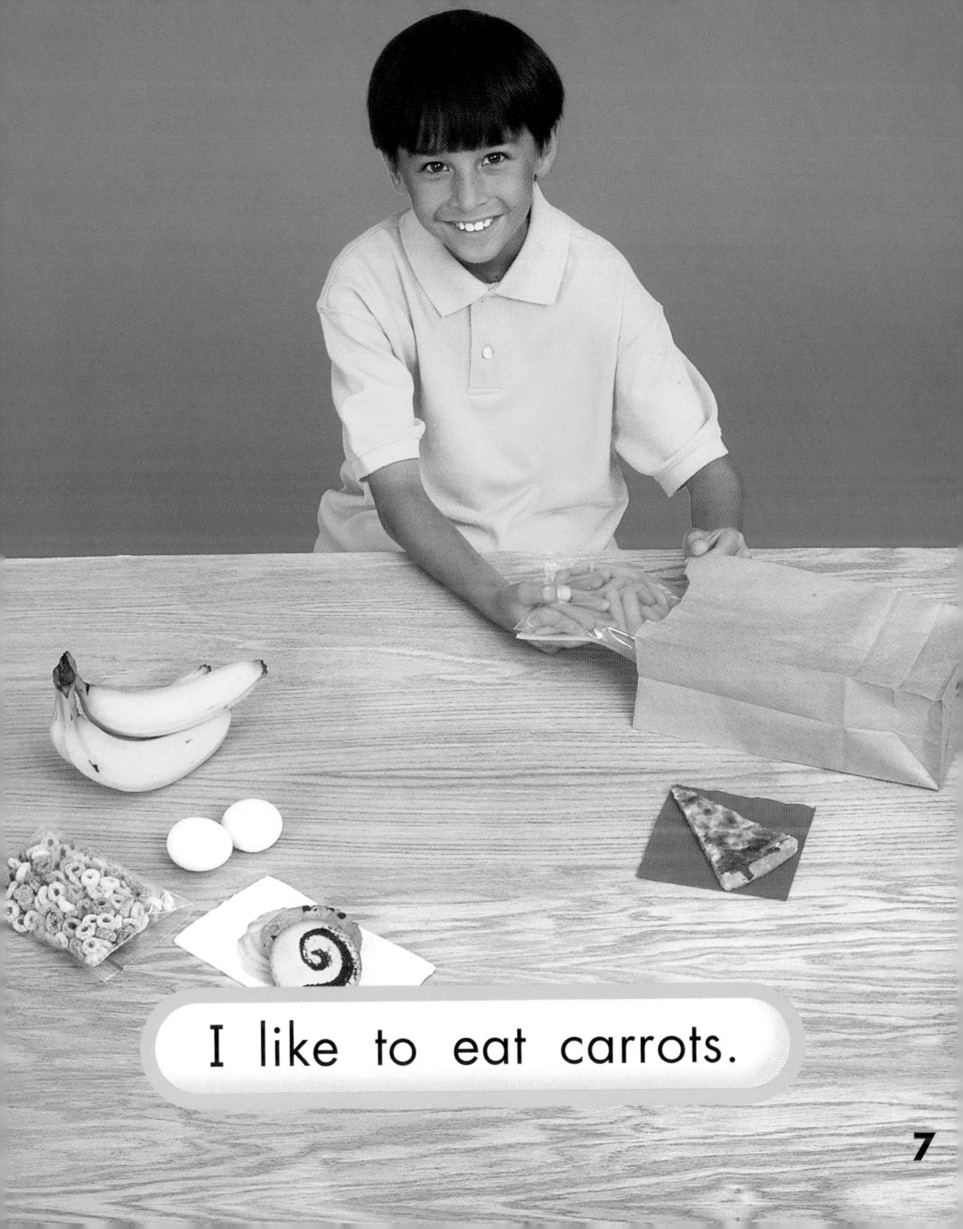

I like to eat carrots.

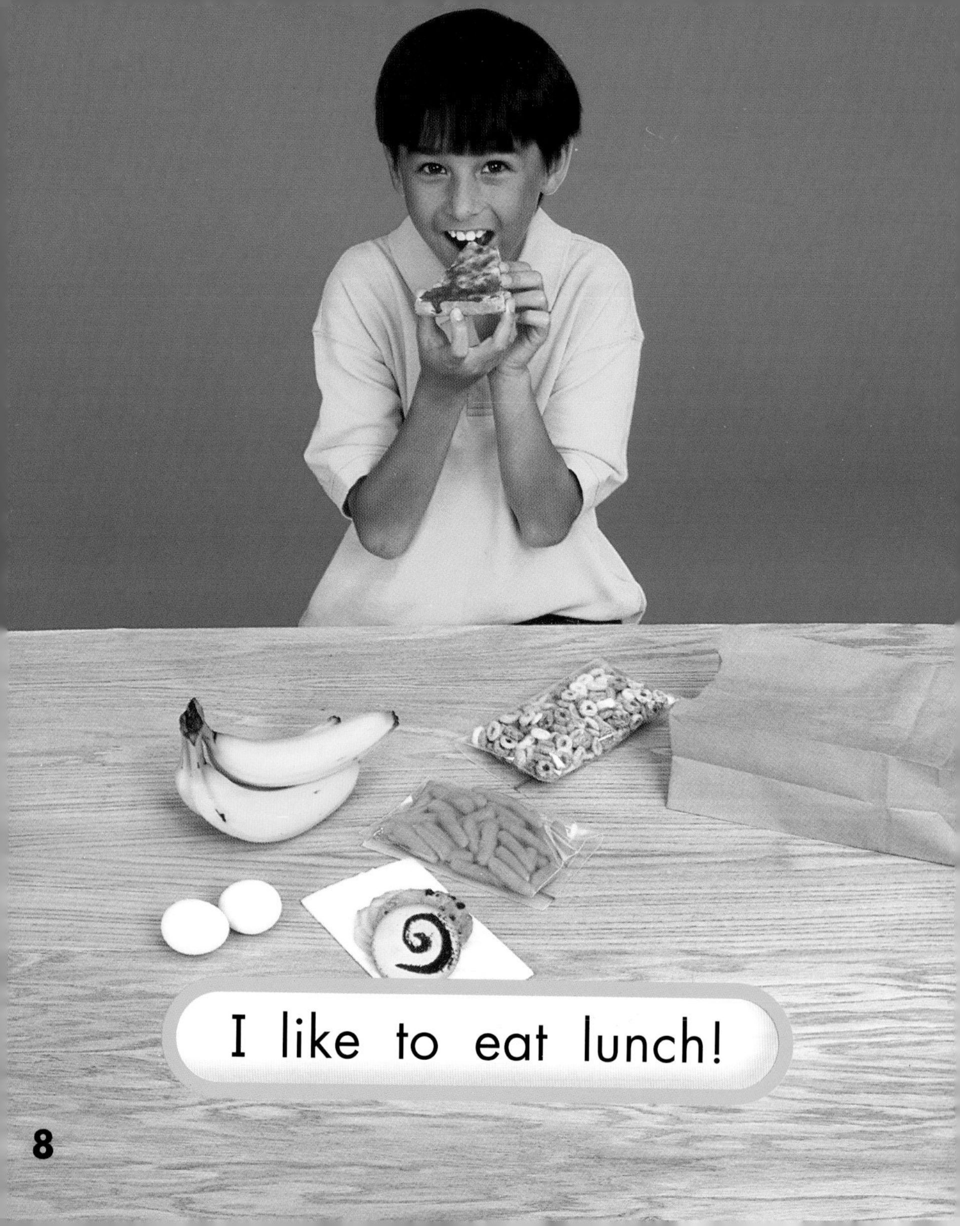

I like to eat lunch!